- If you see "use information from the text and your own ideas", it means that you can use specific details from the reading selection and at the same time include your prior knowledge and experience of the topic in your answer.

WRITING

- Read the instruction carefully so that you know exactly what you are asked to write about.

- Pay attention to the key words such as "describe" and "explain".

- "Describe" means that you have to use words to tell the reader how something looks and feels. It is like using words to create a mental picture for the reader.

- "Explain" means you have to use words to make clear how something works or why something happens or works the way it does. You need to give supporting details step-by-step.

- Ask yourself the five "W-" and one "H-" questions to generate ideas for your writing. These question words are: who, what, when, why, where, and how.

- Jot down the ideas that come to your mind. Organize them and write a draft.

- After writing, check your spelling, grammar, and punctuation.

Sunflowers

The sunflower plant is a very attractive yellow flower. It gets its name from its yellow sun-like face and also from the ability to rotate its face toward the sun as the sun moves from east to west during the day. With plenty of sun and water, the sunflower can grow over three metres tall.

1

The sunflower is so beautiful that it is often used in flower arrangements. It has been painted by many artists, too.

2

Contents

Test-taking TIPS

General

- Count the number of pages to make sure that there are no missing pages.

- Read the instructions carefully so that you know what to do and how to do it.

- In multiple-choice questions, read all the four options before deciding which is the correct answer.

- Write neatly.

- Always check your answers and writing after you have completed the test.

READING

- Read the text once before reading the questions.

- When reading a question, find out what is being asked.

- Look for clue words.

- Look for the information in the text based on the clue words.

- In multiple-choice questions, look for consistent grammar between the stem (the part with a blank for completion) and the response (the choice to be put into the blank to complete the stem). If it does not sound right, it is probably wrong.

Even the famous artist Vincent Van Gogh did a series of sunflower paintings. The sunflower design is often used in arts and crafts and even fabric for clothing.

However, the sunflower is more than a pretty yellow flower. It is an important farm crop and provides food for people and wildlife. Sunflower seeds are used as a snack food. Birds love sunflower seeds and many people buy black oil sunflower seeds for their bird feeders. **3**

The most important use of the sunflower crop is for sunflower oil. Sunflower oil is extracted from sunflower seeds. It is used for salad dressings, frying, and baking. **4**

So you can see that the sunflower is a beautiful plant and also an excellent source of food. It is a very important crop on prairie farms in Canada. **5**

1

1 What kind of text is this piece of reading?

○ a poem

○ a story

○ an article

○ a piece of news

2 What is the first paragraph of the text mainly about?

○ things that are special about the sunflower

○ how the sunflower gets its name

○ the size of the sunflower

○ how the sunflower can grow tall

3 According to the text, which word shows that Vincent Van Gogh is well-known?

○ series

○ artist

○ famous

○ paintings

4 According to the text, which of the following statements is true?

○ Sunflowers can turn to face the sun.

○ Sunflowers are a snack food.

○ Birds like to feed on sunflowers.

○ Sunflowers are used for baking.

5 Read this sentence from paragraph 1.

The sunflower plant is a very attractive yellow flower.

Which word suggests that the author likes sunflowers?

- ○ very
- ○ attractive
- ○ yellow
- ○ flower

6 Read this sentence from paragraph 2.

The sunflower design is often used in arts and crafts and even fabric for clothing.

The word "fabric" means

- ○ drawing.
- ○ cloth.
- ○ weaving.
- ○ needlework.

7 According to the text, which of the following statements is NOT true?

- ○ Sunflowers are a farm crop.
- ○ People like using sunflowers in flower arrangements.
- ○ Sunflowers can grow to a height of over three metres.
- ○ Black oil sunflower seeds are good for making salad.

A Letter from Angela

35 Mountain Trail

Québec City, Quebec

February 12, 2008

Dear Aunt Polly,

Here we are in beautiful Mount St. Anne, Quebec.   **1**
I can't believe that I have learned to ski in just one
day! I thought it would be much harder and scarier
than it was.

First, we booked lessons with our instructor and then   **2**
we were fitted for boots, skis, and poles. It was difficult
to walk in them, but with Dad's help, I managed to
make it to meet our instructor, Jean-Luc.

Jean-Luc first taught me how to fall down and to   **3**
stand back up again. We practised stopping by
pointing the toes of our skis so that it looked like a
slice of pizza. Then we were ready to go on the lift.

The view on the top of the hill was spectacular, but I   4
was pretty nervous about how I would make it down
the hill. Jean-Luc helped me get off the lift and took
me over to the beginner hill. Together, we carefully
made our way down the hill. I was having so much fun
I didn't even notice that we were picking up speed.
Before I knew it, we had reached the bottom and I was
ready to try it all over again.

Mom and Dad were really impressed to see me ski.   5
They took lots of pictures and clapped for me at the
end of the day. I can hardly wait to go back tomorrow.

Maybe this time, I'll try a   6
bigger hill.

                    Love,

                    Angela

2

1 Why does Angela end the following sentence with an exclamation mark?

I can't believe that I have learned to ski in just one day!

- ○ to show that she was surprised
- ○ to show that she wanted to learn more about skiing
- ○ to describe how good she was at skiing
- ○ to end the sentence with style

2 Read this part of the sentence from paragraph 2.

It was difficult to walk in them,

The word "them" refers to

- ○ snow.
- ○ boots.
- ○ boots and skis.
- ○ poles.

3 Read this sentence from paragraph 3.

We practised stopping by pointing the toes of our skis so that it looked like a slice of pizza.

In this sentence, the words "a slice of pizza" mean

- ○ an inverted V shape.
- ○ a W shape.
- ○ a Y shape.
- ○ a U shape.

4 Which of the following sentences from the letter shows that Angela was worried about her first ski downhill?

- ○ I thought it would be much harder and scarier than it was.
- ○ I was pretty nervous about how I would make it down the hill.
- ○ I managed to make it to meet our instructor, Jean-Luc.
- ○ Together, we carefully made our way down the hill.

5 Which of the following words best describes Angela's first skiing trip?

- ○ entertaining
- ○ exciting
- ○ joyful
- ○ impressive

6 Who were on the skiing trip?

- ○ Angela, Angela's parents, and Aunt Polly
- ○ Jean-Luc, Angela's parents, and Angela
- ○ Angela's mom and dad, Angela, and Aunt Polly
- ○ Angela, Aunt Polly, Jean-Luc

Making Tomato Sauce

Labour Day weekend is the most important time   1
of the year for the Romano family. Every year
on this weekend, the entire family gather
together to make their supply of tomato sauce.
They will make enough to last the whole year!
They will give some to Grandpa and Grandma
too.

It was no exception this year. Mrs. Romano   2
was busy cleaning the huge stainless steel
pots in which the tomatoes would be cooked.
Mr. Romano was preparing the outdoor stove

which would be used to heat the pots. Their two daughters, Janet and Martha, had the job of washing the tomatoes.

Once the tomatoes were washed, the family   3
sat down at the table and began to cut the tomatoes into chunks. The chunks were then placed into the pots. When they had filled one, Mr. and Mrs. Romano worked together to lift it onto the stove. The pot was slowly heated until the tomatoes started to boil. Mrs. Romano would then add some special ingredients to the tomatoes and stood by the stove stirring and watching them turn into a thick sauce.

When the tomato sauce was ready, one   4
important thing had to be done. The sauce had to be tasted. Mrs. Romano boiled some pasta and topped it with freshly made sauce. She gave a bowl to each family member and together, they sampled the result of their hard work. After one taste, all four of the Romanos smiled, satisfied with what they had done. The tomato sauce was ready to be put into glass jars.

Yummy!
Yummy!

1 Which of the following sentences shows that the Romano family makes tomato sauce every year?

- ○ Labour Day weekend is the most important time of the year for the Romano family.

- ○ It was no exception this year.

- ○ They will make enough to last the whole year!

- ○ They will give some to Grandpa and Grandma too.

2 Which of the following phrases shows that the tomato sauce was tasty?

- ○ freshly made sauce

- ○ ready to be put into glass jars

- ○ sampled the result of their hard work

- ○ satisfied with what they had done

3 According to the story, the Romano family was making tomato sauce

- ○ in the kitchen.

- ○ in the park.

- ○ outdoors.

- ○ indoors.

4 Read this sentence from paragraph 4.

She gave a bowl to each family member and together, they sampled the result of their hard work.

The word "sampled" means

○ examined.

○ tasted.

○ enjoyed.

○ tested.

5 Who did the actual cooking of the tomato sauce?

○ Mr. Romano

○ Mrs. Romano

○ Janet

○ Martha

6 Which of the following would be the best new title for the story?

○ How to Make Tomato Sauce

○ The Romanos' "Tomato Sauce" Day

○ A Labour Day Weekend

○ Homemade Tomato Sauce

The Food Chain

The simple garden shows how a food chain   1
works. Suppose you have lettuce growing in your
garden. That lettuce gets energy from sunlight.
It also soaks up water and nutrients from the
soil. It now has everything it needs to grow.
Think of this lettuce as the first link in a garden
food chain.

Suppose one night a slug slithers onto the leaf of   2
the lettuce and begins eating it. The energy from
the lettuce is now transferred to the slug. The
slug becomes the second link in the food chain.

In the morning, a beetle comes along, sees the slug and eats it. The energy from the slug is now passed on to the beetle and the beetle becomes the third link in the chain.

Just then, along comes a hungry shrew that eats the beetle. Now the shrew is enjoying all the energy in the chain. But it is not over yet. A wise old owl happens to spot the shrew. It swoops down, picks up the shrew, and returns to its nest to prepare it for dinner. 3

The owl has no natural predators. That means there is no animal that tries to kill the owl for food. The owl is at the top of this food chain and benefits from all the energy passed through all the members of the chain – the lettuce, the slug, the beetle, and the shrew. 4

There are many different food chains in nature. Each environment has its own food chain. We, too, are part of a food chain. Luckily, like the wise old owl, we are also at the top of our chain. 5

4

1 According to the text, which of the following statements is true?

- ○ Human beings are like owls.
- ○ Human beings do not have natural predators.
- ○ Human beings stay at the top of all food chains.
- ○ Human beings are as wise as owls.

2 What is the setting of this text?

- ○ a forest
- ○ a garden
- ○ a field
- ○ a tree

3 According to the text, which of the following is the order of the food chain?

- ○ lettuce, shrew, beetle, slug, owl
- ○ shrew, lettuce, slug, beetle, owl
- ○ lettuce, slug, beetle, shrew, owl
- ○ slug, lettuce, beetle, shrew, owl

4 In paragraph 3, the author uses the phrase "swoops down" to describe the owl's

- ○ swift action.

- ○ quiet movement.

- ○ cautious movement.

- ○ cunning movement.

5 Which of the following statements is NOT true?

- ○ The owl has no natural predators.

- ○ The shrew preys on the beetle.

- ○ Human beings prey on all animals.

- ○ The lettuce gets energy from the sun.

6 Which would be the best new title for this story?

- ○ The Garden Chain

- ○ The Wise Old Owl

- ○ Understanding the Food Chain

- ○ On Top of the Food Chain

The Four-Star Ranch

Helen woke up to the smell of bacon and eggs. 1
For a moment, she thought she was still in her
bed in Vancouver, but then realized that she was
in Calgary at the Four-Star Ranch, owned by her
Aunt Betty and Uncle Steve. Uncle Steve picked
her up at the airport the night before. It had
become a yearly tradition for Helen to spend her
summer vacation helping out on the ranch.

It was half past six and Aunt Betty was making 2
breakfast for the family and wranglers who
worked on the ranch. Helen jumped out of bed,
pulled on her jeans, T-shirt, boots, and cowboy

hat. She quickly said good morning to Aunt Betty on her way out the door. Aunt Betty knew exactly where Helen was going.

Helen was at the barn within seconds. She 3 paused in the doorway to take in the smell of fresh hay. Suddenly, a large head popped over the stall door. Dusty, Helen's horse, stood looking at her with his mouth full of hay. He was just as excited to see her as she was to see him. Helen wrapped her arms around the big brown and white horse and gave him a hug. She could hardly wait to put a saddle on Dusty and take him for a long ride around the farm.

Helen offered Dusty an apple. As he crunched 4 down on the delicious treat, Helen thought about all the fun things she would do with Dusty. They would herd cattle, go galloping through the fields, swim in the pond, and at the end of the day, she would groom him to make him tidy and shiny. All of a sudden, she heard Aunt Betty sounding the breakfast bell. Helen raced back to the house to eat. Her summer adventure had begun.

5

1 According to the story, Helen had been on the ranch for

- ○ a day.
- ○ a night.
- ○ two nights.
- ○ the whole summer.

2 Helen went to visit Dusty

- ○ the night before.
- ○ before breakfast.
- ○ after breakfast.
- ○ in the afternoon.

3 Which of the following would be the best new title for this story?

- ○ Helen and Dusty
- ○ Summer Fun at the Four-Star Ranch
- ○ The Adventure of Helen
- ○ Aunt Betty and Uncle Steve's Ranch

4 Which word means almost the same as the word "galloping"?

- ○ running
- ○ strolling
- ○ walking
- ○ racing

5 Read this sentence from paragraph 2.

Aunt Betty knew exactly where Helen was going.

Where was Helen going?

- ○ to the farm
- ○ to the pond
- ○ to the fields
- ○ to the barn

6 Read this sentence from paragraph 4.

As he crunched down on the delicious treat, Helen thought about all the fun things she would do with Dusty.

In this sentence, the word "treat" means

- ○ bacon.
- ○ eggs.
- ○ hay.
- ○ apple.

7 Which of the following sentences shows that Dusty likes Helen?

- ○ Suddenly, a large head popped over the stall door.
- ○ Helen offered Dusty an apple.
- ○ He was just as excited to see her as she was to see him.
- ○ Helen thought about all the fun things she would do with Dusty.

Hat Day at School

Sean and Rachel are in grade three at Hillside School. Last week, their class had a special fundraising project. They were raising money for the Red Cross. They have been learning about the important work done by the Red Cross when there is a disaster. It is an organization that provides food and supplies for people in need after a disaster such as a hurricane or flood.

1

Sean and Rachel were the leaders of the project. 2
Their job was to collect loonies in a big container
and then roll them into coin holders for the teacher.

Ms. Sharma, their class teacher, had suggested a 3
great way of raising money. Every student would
be allowed to wear a hat at school if they paid a
loonie to the fundraiser. Usually it is the rule to
take off all hats inside the school building.

Rachel had another idea – pay an extra loonie and 4
chew gum at school on Hat Day. Ms. Sharma
agreed that this was also a great idea. On Hat
Day, every student contributed two dollars to the
Red Cross. Many students wore hats of special
design.

It was fun to wear a hat and chew gum at school. 5
Everyone enjoyed Hat Day, including Ms. Sharma.
But best of all, it was good to hear the final count
from Sean and Rachel – the class had raised $98
for the Red Cross disaster fund. Ms. Sharma
congratulated everyone for doing a great job!

6

1 According to the story, which of the following statements is true?

○ Ms. Sharma was the leader of the fundraising project.

○ Ms. Sharma was Rachel's teacher.

○ Ms. Sharma was from the Red Cross.

○ Ms. Sharma collected $98.

2 According to the story, which of the following statements is NOT true?

○ Sean and Rachel led a fundraising project.

○ Students each paid $1 to wear a hat on Hat Day.

○ Students each paid $2 to wear a hat and chew gum on Hat Day.

○ Hillside School had collected $98 for the Red Cross.

3 Which of the following statements shows that Ms. Sharma was happy with the fundraising?

○ Everyone enjoyed Hat Day, including Ms. Sharma.

○ Ms. Sharma congratulated everyone for doing a great job!

○ Ms. Sharma, their class teacher, had suggested a great way of raising money.

○ Ms. Sharma agreed that this was also a great idea.

4 Read this sentence from paragraph 4.

Ms. Sharma agreed that this was also a great idea.

What was "a great idea"?

○ wearing a hat

○ having a Hat Day

○ paying one dollar for chewing gum

○ paying one dollar for wearing a hat

5 Read this sentence from paragraph 4.

On Hat Day, every student contributed two dollars to the Red Cross.

In this sentence, the word "contributed" means almost the same as

○ found.

○ donated.

○ saved.

○ paid.

6 What is the main idea of this story?

○ A grade three class raised money for the Red Cross.

○ It was a fun Hat Day.

○ Rachel suggested having gum on Hat Day.

○ Ms. Sharma came up with the idea of a Hat Day.

Recycling Rules

Remember when you throw away,

Use your bins for Recycling Day.

Plastic, glass, styrofoam too,

Put them in the box that's blue.

Cardboard, magazines, papers thrown away, 5

They go in the box that's grey.

Fruit and veggies; meat and lard,

Go in the green bin; it's not hard.

Recycle bins – green, grey, and blue,

They'll save the world for me and you. 10

Don't overload your garbage can,

Recycle, recycle, whenever you can.

1 According to the poem, which statement is true?

- ○ Food scraps go in the grey box.
- ○ Water bottles should go in the blue box.
- ○ The green bin is for veggies only.
- ○ Garbage is picked up on Garbage Day.

2 Why does the author use an apostrophe for "that's" in line 4?

- ○ to separate the "s" from "that"
- ○ to show how to read the poem
- ○ to make the poem sound better
- ○ to show that a letter has been left out

3 Which of the following words is in short form?

- ○ recycle
- ○ papers
- ○ lard
- ○ veggies

7

4 What do cardboard and magazines have in common?

- They can both be thrown away.
- They are paper products.
- They both go in the blue box.
- They don't overload the garbage can.

5 According to the poem, which statement is NOT true?

- We help save the world by recycling.
- We should know where to put the things for recycling.
- It is easy to remember the recycling rules.
- We should put food scraps in the blue box.

6 Read the line below.

Don't overload your garbage can,

Which of the following lines goes best with it?

- Recycling is the best way to go.
- Follow closely the recycling plan.
- Let's join hands to save the world.
- You must remember to recycle.

7 Do you think "Recycling Rules" is a good title for this poem? Explain why you think so. Use information from the text and your own ideas in your answer.

_____

_____

_____

_____

_____

_____

8 After reading the poem, what are your feelings about recycling? Use information from the text and your own ideas in your answer.

_____

_____

_____

_____

_____

_____

Larry's Outing to a Castle

Larry sat at the back of the yellow school bus.   1
He was very excited. It was a long and bumpy
ride but it was all worth it. Today, Larry and his
classmates were visiting a real castle.

The bus finally came to a stop in front of a   2
magnificent building. Larry could not believe his
eyes. The castle was just like the ones that he

had seen in books and movies. The children walked excitedly across a drawbridge and reached the entrance to the castle.

Mr. Greene greeted the students at the entrance. He was going to take them on a tour through the castle. He explained to the children that they would be seeing many old and interesting artifacts. He also reminded them not to wander off alone because it was very easy to get lost in this old, enormous castle and there were some parts of the castle that were off limits to visitors.

3

Larry was not listening; he was far too busy staring at something standing at the end of a long corridor. Then he slowly moved closer to examine the object. It was a large, silver suit of armour. Beside the armour was a closed door with a sign. On the sign were the words, "DO NOT ENTER". Larry could not resist the temptation. He felt his hand moving toward the doorknob...

4

8

1 Which of the following shows that Larry was looking eagerly forward to the trip to the castle?

- ○   it was all worth it
- ○   a long and bumpy ride
- ○   a magnificent building
- ○   many old and interesting artifacts

2 Why does the story end with "..."?

- ○   to show that Larry was nervous
- ○   to let readers think what would happen next
- ○   to show that the door could not be opened
- ○   to show that Larry did not know what to do next

3 Read this sentence from paragraph 4.

Larry could not resist the temptation.

What was the temptation?

- ○   to examine the armour
- ○   to put on the armour
- ○   to take off the "DO NOT ENTER" sign
- ○   to open the door

4 Which would be the best new title for this story?

- ○ Mischievous Larry
- ○ Larry's Adventure in the Castle
- ○ A Memorable Outing
- ○ An Exciting Trip

5 Explain what kind of person you think Larry is and tell why you think so. Use information from the story and your own ideas in your answer.

_____

_____

_____

_____

_____

6 What do you think might happen when Larry turned the doorknob?

_____

_____

_____

_____

_____

Trees

Have you ever noticed the many kinds of trees   1
we see every day? Some trees have broad leaves
that turn brown and drop off in the fall. These
are called deciduous trees. Other trees have
narrow leaves that stay green on the trees all
year round. We call these coniferous trees.

All trees have trunks to support them and bark   2
to protect the trunk from insects and diseases.
What is interesting about tree trunks is that the
trunk can tell the age of the tree. When the trunk
is cut, it shows rings and by counting the rings,

we can tell how many years the tree has been alive. One ring represents one year.

People use trees for food, housing, furniture, paper, and a variety of wooden objects. Fruit trees such as apple, peach, and pear give us food to eat. Softwood trees grow quickly, so they provide most of the wood used for building houses. Softwood comes from coniferous trees such as pine and spruce. The wood from hardwood trees is more expensive because it may take up to a hundred years before they grow big enough to be used. Some well-known hardwood trees are walnut, oak, maple, and beech. These woods are often used for making furniture.

3

Trees have grown in nature for thousands of years. They are important to the environment because they give off oxygen that all human beings and animals need for breathing. Trees also provide homes for wildlife. Every year, tens of thousands of trees are being cut down for people to use. It is important to replace these trees by growing new ones so that trees will always be available in the future.

4

9

1 Using information from the text, list four things that are different between deciduous trees and coniferous trees.

TREES

Deciduous   Coniferous

2 Give two examples to show how trees are also important to animals. Use information from the text.

_____

_____

_____

_____

_____

3 Explain why it is important to plant new trees. Use information from the text and your own ideas in your answer.

_____

_____

_____

_____

_____

_____

_____

4 What would happen if people used hardwood for building houses?

_____

_____

_____

_____

_____

_____

_____

Country Sights

A drive in the country,

What an awesome scene!

Miles and miles of cornfields,

Growing tall and green.

Farmers driving tractors,   5

Under the red hot sun.

Roadside stands with veggies,

Food for everyone!

Tall silos in the distance,

Barns and stables too.   10

Fields piled with haystacks,

Under a sky of blue.

Cows gently grazing,

Horses running free.

Driving in the country,   15

It's where I love to be!

1 According to the poem, which statement is true?

    ○   Farmers drive their tractors through the cornfields.

    ○   There are many cornfields.

    ○   The writer drives through the cornfields.

    ○   Corn is growing next to vegetables.

2 Why does the author use an exclamation mark at the end of line 2?

    ○   to show that the driving is exciting

    ○   to show his excitement about the trip

    ○   to show the spectacular view he sees

    ○   to show that he does not believe in what he sees

10

3 According to the poem, in which season does the author make the trip?

    ○   spring

    ○   summer

    ○   fall

    ○   winter

4 Choose one stanza (section) of the poem. Write it out in complete sentences.

_____

_____

_____

_____

5 Use information from the poem to show that the weather is good when the author visits the countryside.

_____

_____

_____

_____

6 Do you think "Country Sights" is a good title for this poem? Use information from the poem and your own ideas in your answer.

_____

_____

_____

_____

_____

_____

7 After reading the poem, what are your feelings about the countryside? Use information from the poem and your own ideas in your answer.

_____

_____

_____

_____

_____

_____

1 On your way to school, you saw a stray dog on the street. Write a short story. Describe the dog and tell what happened.

─────────── **Ideas for My Story** ───────────

Now write a story, The Stray Dog.

2 Read the sentence. Part of the sentence is missing.

When the doorbell _____, we were having dinner.

Which of the following correctly completes the sentence?

○ ringing

○ rings

○ rang

○ was ringing

3 Which of the following words begins with a prefix?

○ immense

○ important

○ imitate

○ impolite

4 Which word below goes with "tree" to make a compound word?

○ top

○ branch

○ trunk

○ bark

5 Read the sentences below.

The children were at Martha's birthday party. They had birthday cake and yummy food. They played fun games, too.

Which of the following is the best way to combine these sentences?

o At Martha's birthday party, they had birthday cake and yummy food and they played fun games, too.

o The children were at Martha's birthday party, and they had birthday cake and yummy food, and they played fun games, too.

o At Martha's birthday party, the children had birthday cake and yummy food, and they played fun games, too.

o The children at Martha's birthday party had birthday cake, yummy food, and fun games.

6 Which of the following words is NOT correct?

o putting

o sobing

o dyeing

o skiing

1 Your class is planning an outing and your teacher is asking for suggestions of where to go. Write the place you think is best for the outing. Explain why you feel this is the best place to go.

─────────── **Ideas for My Writing** ───────────

Write your suggestion here.

2 Which of the following words begins with a prefix?

- ○ unit
- ○ under
- ○ undo
- ○ unite

3 Choose the word in the sentence that describes the man.

The old man pointed to a box near him.

- ○ pointed
- ○ old
- ○ near
- ○ him

4 Read the sentence below.

They enjoy _____ baseball after school.

Which of the following words correctly completes the sentence?

- ○ play
- ○ plays
- ○ playing
- ○ played

5 Read the sentence below.

Mrs. Baker let the children share the candies _____ themselves.

Which of the following words correctly completes the sentence?

○   with

○   among

○   for

○   between

6 Read the sentences below.

Ming can't find his journal. Ming looks everywhere. His sister looks everywhere for him too.

Which of the following is the best way to combine these sentences?

○   Ming and his sister look everywhere but they can't find Ming's journal.

○   Ming can't find his journal and he looks everywhere and his sister looks eveywhere for him too.

○   Ming's sister and Ming look everywhere for his journal but Ming's sister and Ming can't find his journal.

○   Ming looks everywhere and his sister looks everywhere and they can't find his journal.

1　Your parents will give you a pet for your birthday.

Write about the pet that you would like to have. Explain why you want this pet and how you would take care of it.

——————————— **Ideas for My Writing** ———————————

2 Read the sentence below.

We will _____ at the hotel for two nights.

Which of the following correctly completes the sentence?

- ○ stay
- ○ to stay
- ○ staying
- ○ be stay

3 Read the sentence below.

We have not _____ each other for a long time.

Which of the following words correctly completes the sentence?

- ○ see
- ○ saw
- ○ seeing
- ○ seen

4 Which of the following words is NOT a compound word?

- ○ beginner
- ○ housekeeper
- ○ salesman
- ○ woodpecker

5 Choose the word in the sentence that describes the children.

The drama teacher thinks that the children are too timid.

- ○ thinks

- ○ timid

- ○ drama

- ○ too

6 Read the sentences below.

We went on a field trip yesterday. It was fun. We enjoyed ourselves very much.

Which of the following is the best way to combine these sentences?

- ○ We went on a field trip yesterday and it was fun and we enjoyed ourselves very much.

- ○ We went on a field trip yesterday so we enjoyed ourselves very much and it was fun.

- ○ We enjoyed ourselves very much on a field trip yesterday and it was fun.

- ○ Yesterday's field trip was fun and we enjoyed ourselves very much.

1 Write a short story. In your story, there should be a little boy, an ice cream, and a squirrel.

—————————— **Ideas for My Story** ——————————

4

2 Read the sentence below. Part of the sentence is missing.

Jay always _____ the books on time.

Which of the following correctly completes the sentence?

- ○ return
- ○ returns
- ○ returning
- ○ is returning

3 Read the sentence below. Part of the sentence is missing.

She came home _____ and her mother was worried.

Which of the following words correctly completes the sentence?

- ○ late
- ○ lately
- ○ later
- ○ latest

4 Which word below goes with "cake" to make a compound word?

- ○ birthday
- ○ cup
- ○ chocolate
- ○ wedding

5 Choose the word in the sentence that describes how the children were singing.

The little children were singing sweetly in the school concert.

- ○   sweetly
- ○   little
- ○   concert
- ○   school

6 Read the sentences below.

We can have a game of baseball after school. We can watch a video after school. We can only choose one to do after school.

Which of the following is the best way to combine these sentences?

- ○   We can have a game of baseball after school and we can watch a video after school and we can only choose one to do.

- ○   We can either have a game of baseball or watch a video after school.

- ○   We can have a game of baseball after school or we can watch a video and we can only choose one to do.

- ○   We can have a game of baseball or we can watch a video after school but we can only choose one to do after school.

LANGUAGE

Assessment of Reading and Writing

Grade

3

Grandma's Quilt

My grandmother lives on a farm and I love to visit her there. She has lots of antique furniture and many interesting old items. One of my favourite things is an old quilt that was made over fifty years ago. 5
Grandma had it when she was a little girl and she calls it her "story quilt". Her mother made it with different patches of material. Each square of cloth came from old clothing or household items and Grandma has a 10
story to tell about each piece. The quilt is like a record of the family past.

There is a green velvet square from Grandma's favourite skirt and some corduroy fabric from her brother's overalls. 15 There is a square of white satin from a wedding dress and a piece of embroidered linen from an old pillow case. There are quite a few squares of flowered material from the colourful dresses the little girls 20 used to wear. In the centre of the quilt, there is a beautiful rose design. Grandma told me that it was once a tapestry cushion from the front parlour. One day, the cat tore the cushion so her mother saved the 25 rose for her quilt.

I think that this quilt, which was made from old scraps of material, is worth more than all the brand new bedding we buy today. It is warm and cozy and pretty but best of all, 30 it has a story to tell.

1 Which word means almost the same as "antique"?

- ○ beautiful
- ○ old
- ○ expensive
- ○ comfortable

2 According to the text, which of the following statements is true?

- ○ Some corduroy fabric was from a wedding dress.
- ○ The rose design was from Grandma's pillow.
- ○ A green velvet square was from a cushion.
- ○ There was a patch of linen from a pillow case.

3 Read this sentence from the text (lines 6–7).

Grandma had it when she was a little girl and she calls it her "story quilt".

The quotation marks are used to show that

- ○ the quilt can tell stories.
- ○ "story quilt" is a special name given to the quilt by Grandma.
- ○ the quilt is like a storybook.
- ○ the quilt is as interesting as a story.

4 Which of the following statements is NOT true?

- ○ Grandma's mother made the quilt for Grandma.
- ○ Grandma made the quilt when she was very young.
- ○ The author likes the story quilt very much.
- ○ The story quilt was made from old scraps of material.

5 Read this sentence from the text (lines 9–11).

Each square of cloth came from old clothing or household items and Grandma has a story to tell about each piece.

Which of the following are household items?

- ○ overalls
- ○ wedding dresses
- ○ cushions
- ○ skirts

6 What kind of text is this piece of reading?

- ○ a report
- ○ a journal entry
- ○ a story
- ○ a letter

7 Which would be the best new title for this text?

○ Grandma's Story Quilt

○ The Old Story Quilt

○ A Record of the Family Past

○ A Quilt You Can't Buy

8 Read this sentence from the text (lines 27–29).

I think that this quilt, which was made from old scraps of material, is worth more than all the brand new bedding we buy today.

Explain why the author thinks this way. Use information from the text and your own ideas in your answer.

_____

_____

_____

_____

_____

_____

_____

_____

9 Write a paragraph about a toy that you like best. Describe how it looks. Tell how you got it and why you love it so much.

—————————— **Ideas for My Paragraph** ——————————

10 Read this sentence.

I have never seen such a colourful quilt before.

Which of the following words describes "quilt"?

- O never
- O seen
- O such
- O colourful

11 Which of the following words has a prefix?

- O divide
- O discover
- O dish
- O distance

12 Which of the following is a compound word?

- O handyman
- O mango
- O many
- O mantis

13 Which of the following belongs in this sentence?

They _____ a group dance before the concert.

○ performs

○ performing

○ will perform

○ are perform

14 Which of the following best completes this sentence?

I saw _____ stranger waiting outside the office.

○ a

○ an

○ this

○ that

15 Which of the following best completes this sentence?

Janet did not know _____.

○ he

○ him

○ his

○ himself

Water Safety

Playing in water is fun but it can be dangerous if you do not pay attention to safety.

The first rule of water safety is to be always with a buddy. If you have a problem, your friend can come to your rescue or go and get help.

5

Also, it is best to have an adult present, especially if you are not good at swimming. You should never swim at a beach where there is no lifeguard or adult.

10

Swimming pools are usually well supervised but you can still get injured if you are not careful. Most injuries are a result of running carelessly and slipping on wet surfaces. You should avoid chasing and running on the pool side. If you are a beginning swimmer, you should stay in the shallow end of the pool.

15

If you want to swim in a river or a lake, find out what is below the water surface before plunging in. Often there are submerged rocks or branches that you can't see. If you jump or dive into unknown waters, you may seriously injure yourself on a hidden object.

20

If you are at a cottage, you may have the chance to go boating. When you are in a boat, you should always wear a life jacket.

25

16 Read this sentence from the text (lines 16–18).

If you are a beginning swimmer, you should stay in the shallow end of the pool.

Which of the following means the opposite of "shallow"?

○ dangerous

○ deep

○ wide

○ narrow

17 Read this sentence from the text (lines 21–22).

Often there are submerged rocks or branches that you can't see.

Which of the following means almost the same as "submerged"?

○ underwater

○ big

○ sharp

○ dangerous

18 According to the text, which of the following statements is true?

○ We should not swim in rivers or lakes.

○ There may be hidden objects in rivers or lakes.

○ We should only swim in swimming pools.

○ We should wear life jackets when we swim.

19 On your way home from school, you saw a backpack hanging from a tree.

Write a paragraph about what you would do.

—— **Ideas for My Paragraph** ——

20 Read this sentence.

Yesterday he _____ home for school at about seven o'clock.

Which of the following best completes the sentence?

- ○ left
- ○ leave
- ○ leaves
- ○ leaving

21 Read this sentence.

The birthday party began at four in the afternoon and the children played _____ seven in the evening.

Which of the following best completes the sentence?

- ○ for
- ○ to
- ○ at
- ○ until

22 Which of the following words is wrong in spelling?

- ○ biting
- ○ beatting
- ○ beaten
- ○ bitten

23 Read this sentence.

The tired players were enjoying ice cream cones after the exciting ball game.

Which of the following words describes "ball game"?

○   tired

○   enjoying

○   ice

○   exciting

24 Read the sentences below.

Summer is hot and sunny. The boys enjoy swimming in the pool. The pool is in John's backyard.

Which of the following is the best way to combine these sentences?

○   In the hot and sunny summer, the boys enjoy swimming in the pool in John's backyard.

○   Summer is hot and sunny, and the boys enjoy swimming in the pool; the pool is in John's backyard.

○   In the hot and sunny summer, the boys enjoy swimming in the pool and the pool is in John's backyard.

○   Summer is hot and sunny, and the boys enjoy swimming in the pool in John's backyard.

Reading Practice 1

1. an article
2. things that are special about the sunflower
3. famous
4. Sunflowers can turn to face the sun.
5. attractive
6. cloth
7. Black oil sunflower seeds are good for making salad.

Reading Practice 2

1. to show that she was surprised
2. boots and skis.
3. an inverted V shape.
4. I was pretty nervous about how I would make it down the hill.
5. exciting
6. Jean-Luc, Angela's parents, and Angela

Reading Practice 3

1. It was no exception this year.
2. satisfied with what they had done
3. outdoors.
4. tasted.
5. Mrs. Romano
6. The Romanos' "Tomato Sauce" Day

Reading Practice 4

1. Human beings do not have natural predators.
2. a garden
3. lettuce, slug, beetle, shrew, owl
4. swift action.
5. Human beings prey on all animals.
6. The Garden Chain

Reading Practice 5

1. a night.
2. before breakfast.
3. Summer Fun at the Four-Star Ranch
4. running
5. to the barn
6. apple.
7. He was just as excited to see her as she was to see him.

Reading Practice 6

1. Ms. Sharma was Rachel's teacher.
2. Hillside School had collected $98 for the Red Cross.
3. Everyone enjoyed Hat Day, including Ms. Sharma.
4. paying one dollar for chewing gum
5. donated.
6. A grade three class raised money for the Red Cross.

Reading Practice 7

1. Water bottles should go in the blue box.
2. to show that a letter has been left out
3. veggies
4. They are paper products.
5. We should put food scraps in the blue box.
6. Follow closely the recycling plan.
7-8. (Individual answers)

Reading Practice 8

1. it was all worth it
2. to let readers think what would happen next
3. to open the door
4. Larry's Adventure in the Castle
5-6. (Individual answers)

Reading Practice 9

1.
```
          TREES
Deciduous          Coniferous
```
Deciduous	Coniferous
• broad leaves	• narrow leaves
• leaves turn brown and drop off in the fall	• leaves stay green on the tree all year round
• hardwood	• softwood
• used for making furniture	• used for building houses

2. Trees give off oxygen that animals need for breathing.
   Trees provide homes for wildlife.
3-4. (Individual answers)

Reading Practice 10

1. There are many cornfields.
2. to show the spectacular view he sees
3. summer
4-7. (Individual answers)

Writing Practice 1

1. (Individual writing)
2. rang
3. impolite
4. treetop
5. The children at Martha's birthday party had birthday cake, yummy food, and fun games.
6. sobing

Writing Practice 2

1. (Individual writing)
2. undo
3. old
4. playing
5. among
6. Ming and his sister look everywhere but they can't find Ming's journal.

Writing Practice 3

1. (Individual writing)
2. stay   3. seen
4. beginner   5. timid
6. Yesterday's field trip was fun and we enjoyed ourselves very much.

Writing Practice 4

1. (Individual writing)
2. returns
3. late
4. cupcake
5. sweetly
6. We can either have a game of baseball or watch a video after school.

Assessment of Reading and Writing

1. old
2. There was a patch of linen from a pillow case.
3. "story quilt" is a special name given to the quilt by Grandma.
4. Grandma made the quilt when she was very young.
5. cushions
6. a story
7. Grandma's Story Quilt
8. (Individual answer)
9. (Individual writing)
10. colourful   11. discover
12. handyman   13. will perform
14. a   15. him
16. deep   17. underwater
18. There may be hidden objects in rivers or lakes.
19. (Individual writing)
20. left   21. until
22. beatting   23. exciting
24. In the hot and sunny summer, the boys enjoy swimming in the pool in John's backyard.